SPANISH & ENGLISH LEARNING CENTER ACTIVITIES

This book provides bilingual materials to create over 50 learning centers about a variety of themes. Included is a teacher's instruction section with details for each project along with ideas to use throughout the classroom. Students will complete hands-on activities while practicing skills in reading, math, and spelling. Both Spanish and English versions of each project are included in one book!

Cover Photos:
Photo www.comstock.com
© 1995 PhotoDisc Incorporated

ISBN 1-59441-640-0

Introduction

The Spanish and English learning centers in this book are grouped into two main curriculum areas. Language arts activities are found on pages 3–19; math activities are on pages 20–27. There are assembly instructions for creating each center using the materials provided as well as student directions for completing the activity. Because both Spanish and English activity pages are included for each center, you may choose a variety of combinations of pictures and Spanish and English words depending upon the skills you wish to emphasize and students' ability levels. You may copy additional activity pages on 8½" x 11" (21.5 cm x 28 cm) white paper. Then, after students have completed the center activity, use the pages as assessment tools, review sheets for classroom discussions, or homework assignments.

Assembly Instructions for Cards

Copy the desired pages onto colorful, sturdy paper and laminate for permanent use in the center. If appropriate, copy a combination of English and/or Spanish pages. Cut apart and store in resealable plastic bags.

Assembly Instructions for Student Journals and ABC Dictionaries

Supply sturdy paper or construction paper for journal or dictionary covers. For journal inside pages, copy page 77 on 8½" x 11" (21.5 cm x 28 cm) white paper. Make two-sided copies for writing-only activities. Make one-sided copies for activities that require both writing and drawing or gluing. (When the journal is folded and assembled, students may draw or glue on the back of the next lined page.) For dictionaries, make two-sided copies of pages 78–79. Plain sheets of paper may be added for illustrations. Bind the journals or dictionaries using brass fasteners or staples. Have students decorate the covers to complement the theme or topic of the activity.

The student journals and dictionaries will be used for a variety of center projects. They also make great take-home projects. Have students share their finished journals or dictionaries with the class.

Students can also write stories or facts about the topics in their journals. Have students complete several journals to create their own libraries. Finished journals also make excellent themed bulletin board displays.

Language Arts
Learning Center Activities (pages 3–19)

Story Maker (pages 28–29, 32–33, and 77)

Objective: Creating Rebus Stories

Assembly Instructions
1. Copy activity pages 28–29 or 32–33 onto colorful, sturdy paper for each student.
2. Cut each page into eight separate pictures. Do not use the word choices.
3. Place the pictures in a plastic or paper bag.
4. Copy page 77 onto white paper for each student.
5. Place glue, pencils, and the bag in the center.
6. Combine the finished stories into a class big book.

Student Directions
1. Draw four picture cards from the bag.
2. Use the pictures to create a rebus story.
3. On the lined paper, write the story and glue the pictures where they belong.
4. Exchange the story with a friend.

Last Letter Makes the First Letter (pages 30–31)

Objective: Identifying Beginning and Ending Sounds

Assembly Instructions
1. Copy activity page 30 or 31 onto colorful paper.
2. Cut the page into strips. Each strip should feature one word and its corresponding picture.
3. Glue each strip to a 5" x 7" (12.5 cm x 18 cm) index card.

Student Directions
1. Find three friends to play.
2. Take turns. Choose a card.
3. Tell the missing beginning sound of the word. Say the word together.
4. Tell the ending sound of the word.
5. Think of another word that starts with the ending sound.
6. If you are right, keep the card. The player with the most cards wins.

What Sentences Can You Make? (pages 56–57 and 77)

Objective: Making Complete Sentences

Assembly Instructions

1. Copy activity page 56 or 57 onto colorful, sturdy paper. Laminate for durability.
2. Cut the page into separate words.
3. Follow the instructions on page 2 for student journals.

Student Directions

1. Place the word cards faceup on a desktop.
2. Arrange the words to make a sentence.
3. Write the sentence in your journal.
4. See how many new sentences you can make. Write them in your journal.

Match It Up (pages 56–57 and 77)

Objective: Recognizing Vocabulary and Sight Words

Assembly Instructions

1. Make two copies of activity page 56 or 57 on two different colors of sturdy paper. Laminate for durability.
2. Cut one of the pages into sentence strips.
3. Attach one side of a small piece of hook-and-loop tape to the sentence strip above each word in the sentence. Place the strips in a sentence strip chart.
4. Cut the remaining page into separate words. Attach the other side of the hook-and-loop tape to the back of each word.
5. Select the words students will review and place these words in a paper or plastic bag.
6. Follow the instructions on page 2 for student journals.

Student Directions

1. Draw one word card from the bag.
2. Find the matching word in the sentence strip.
3. Attach the word card to the matching word on the sentence strip.
4. Continue until all of the word cards are matched.
5. Write the words in your journal.

Vocabulary Clap (pages 28–29 or 32–33)

Objective: Identifying Syllables

Assembly Instructions

1. Copy activity page 28, 29, 32, or 33 onto colorful paper.
2. Cut the page into strips. Each strip should feature the correctly spelled word and its corresponding picture.
3. Glue each strip to a 3" x 5" (7.5 cm x 12.5 cm) index card.

Student Directions

1. Find a partner.
2. Choose a card.
3. Say the word together.
4. Say the word again and clap the syllables you hear.

Who Am I? (pages 38–40 and 77)

Objective: Identifying Words

Assembly Instructions

1. Copy activity pages 40 and 38 or 39 onto colorful, sturdy paper. Laminate for durability.
2. Cut the pages into separate words and pictures.
3. Follow the instructions on page 2 for student journals.

Student Directions

1. Find a partner.
2. Place the word and picture cards faceup on a desktop.
3. Take turns. Choose a picture card.
4. Find the word that matches the picture.
5. Write the word and draw the picture in your journal.

What Order? (pages 30–31 and 77)

Objective: Alphabetizing Words

Assembly Instructions

1. Copy activity page 30 or 31 onto colorful, sturdy paper. Laminate for durability.
2. Cut the page into strips. Each strip should feature one word and its corresponding picture.
3. Place the strips and a write-on/wipe-away marker in the center.
4. Follow the instructions on page 2 for student journals.

Student Directions

1. Choose a word strip.
2. Fill in the missing letter in the word.
3. Repeat with all of the words.
4. Put the words in alphabetical order.
5. Write the words in alphabetical order in your journal.

I Can Write It (pages 34–35)

Objectives: Forming Letters; Recognizing Vocabulary Words

Assembly Instructions

1. Copy activity page 34 or 35 onto colorful paper.
2. Cut the page into separate cards. Glue each card to a 3" x 5" (7.5 cm x 12.5 cm) index card.
3. Place the cards in a plastic or paper bag. Or, punch a hole in each card and put the cards on a ring.
4. Place the cards and a variety of markers, chalk, colorful pencils, crayons, paper, white boards, and chalkboards in the center.

Student Directions

1. Choose one card.
2. Choose the materials you want to use to write the word.
3. Write the word. Then, draw a picture of the word.
4. Choose another word. Write and draw a picture of the word.

Silly Sentences (pages 36–37 and 77)

Objective: Completing Sentences

Assembly Instructions

1. Copy activity page 36 or 37 onto colorful paper.
2. Cut the page into sentence strips.
3. Glue each strip to a 5" x 7" (12.5 cm x 18 cm) index card.
4. Follow the instructions on page 2 for student journals.

Student Directions

1. Choose a card.
2. Write the sentence in your journal.
3. Fill in the blank with a word that makes the sentence silly.
4. Share your silly sentence with a friend.

Read around the Room (page 77)

Objective: Practicing Reading and Writing

Assembly Instructions

1. Display a collection of poems and songs throughout the classroom.
2. Follow the instructions on page 2 for student journals.

Student Directions

1. Find a partner.
2. Choose a poem or song.
3. Point to each word as your partner reads the poem aloud.
4. Copy the poem in your journal. Draw a picture of the poem.
5. Choose another poem. Trade jobs and repeat.

Rhyming Spiders (pages 76–77)

Objective: Identifying Rhyming Words

Assembly Instructions
1. Copy activity page 76 onto colorful, sturdy paper. Laminate for durability.
2. Cut the page into separate picture cards.
3. Copy page 77 onto white paper.

Student Directions
1. Choose a picture card. Count the number of spiders on the card.
2. Write the number of spiders on a piece of paper. Then, write the word for the number.
3. Think of as many words as you can that rhyme with the number word. Write them down.
4. Share your words with a friend.

The "Write" Word (pages 60–61 and 77)

Objective: Defining Vocabulary Words

Assembly Instructions
1. Copy activity page 60 or 61 onto colorful, sturdy paper. Laminate for durability.
2. Cut the page into separate word cards.
3. Place the pictures in a plastic or paper bag.
4. Copy page 77 onto white paper.

Student Directions
1. Draw two to four word cards from the bag.
2. Read the words on the cards.
3. Write each word. Then, write what you know about the word.

ABC Dictionary (pages 28–29 or 32–33 and 78–79)

Objective: Recognizing Beginning Letters

Assembly Instructions

1. Make two copies of activity page 28, 29, 32, or 33 onto colorful paper.
2. Cut one activity page into separate cards. Each card should feature a picture and its corresponding spelling word choices. Glue each card to a 5" x 7" (12.5 cm x 18 cm) index card.
3. Place the word and picture cards in a paper or plastic bag.
4. Follow the instructions on page 2 for student ABC dictionaries.
5. Complete the other activity page to create an answer key. Laminate for durability.

Student Directions

1. Draw one card from the bag.
2. Read the words next to the picture. Choose the correct word.
3. Write the word in the correct place in your dictionary.
4. Continue with another card.
5. Check your answers.

Seek the Sound (pages 62–63 and 77)

Objectives: Identifying Medial Sounds; Identifying Beginning Sounds

Assembly Instructions

1. Make two copies of activity page 62 or 63 onto colorful paper.
2. Cut one activity page into separate strips. Each strip should feature a word and its corresponding picture. Glue each strip to a 5" x 7" (12.5 cm x 18 cm) index card.
3. Place the cards in a paper or plastic bag.
4. Place the bag and a variety of themed books in the center.
5. Follow the instructions on page 2 for student journals.
6. Complete the other activity page to create an answer key. Laminate for durability.

Student Directions

1. Find a partner.
2. Draw one card from the bag.
3. Say the word aloud with your partner. What is the missing letter?
4. Write the missing letter in your journal. Check your answer.
5. Choose a book.
6. Find four words in the book that begin with the missing letter.
7. Write the words in your journal.

Find the Sentence (page 77)

Objective: Identifying Sentences

Assembly Instructions
1. Copy page 77 onto white paper for each student.
2. Place a variety of books of different reading levels in the center.

Student Directions
1. Choose a book.
2. Write the title and author of the book.
3. Find page 3 of the book. Read the first sentence on page 3.
4. Write the sentence. Count the words and write the number.
5. Find the last page of the book. Read the last sentence.
6. Write the sentence. Count the words and write the number.

Syllable Count (pages 34–35 and 77)

Objective: Identifying Two-Syllable Words

Assembly Instructions
1. Copy activity page 34 or 35 onto colorful, sturdy paper. Laminate for durability.
2. Cut the page into separate cards. Each card should feature one picture with or without the corresponding word.
3. Place the pictures in a plastic or paper bag.
4. Follow the instructions on page 2 for student journals.

Student Directions
1. Choose a card.
2. Say the word for the picture aloud.
3. Clap and count the syllables in the word.
4. If the word has two syllables, write the word in your journal.
5. Draw a picture of the word.
6. Choose another card and repeat.

Write the Room (pages 78–79)

Objective: Recognizing Beginning Letters

Assembly Instructions
Follow the instructions on page 2 for student ABC dictionaries.

Student Directions
1. Look for words all around your classroom.
2. Try to find a word that begins with each letter of the alphabet.
3. Write each word in the correct place in your dictionary.
4. Share the words you found with a friend.

ABC Order (pages 34–35 or 70–71 and 78–79)

Objective: Alphabetizing Words

Assembly Instructions
1. Copy activity page 34, 35, 70, or 71 onto colorful, sturdy paper. Laminate for durability.
2. Cut the page into separate cards. Each card should feature a picture and its corresponding word.
3. Follow the instructions on page 2 for student ABC dictionaries.

Student Directions
1. Find two or three partners.
2. Work together to sort the cards into alphabetical order.
3. Write each word in the correct place in your dictionary.

Simple Machines Mobile (pages 51–55)

Objective: Developing Vocabulary

Assembly Instructions

1. Copy the mobile header activity page 54 or 55 onto colorful, sturdy paper for each student. Then, copy the picture cards (page 51) and word cards (page 52 or 53) for each student.
2. Place glue, scissors, yarn, tape, a hole punch, crayons or markers, and the activity pages in the center.

Student Directions

1. Color the mobile header. Cut it out and fold it lengthwise.
2. Color the picture cards. Cut apart the picture cards and the word cards.
3. Glue each word card to the back of the correct picture card.
4. Punch the holes in the mobile header.
5. Attach the cards to the mobile header with yarn and tape.

Hide and Seek (pages 62–63 and 77)

Objective: Identifying Words

Assembly Instructions

1. Copy activity page 62 or 63 onto colorful paper.
2. Cut the page into strips. Each strip should feature one word and its corresponding picture.
3. Glue each strip to a 5" x 7" (12.5 cm x 18 cm) index card.
4. Place the pictures in a plastic or paper bag.
5. Follow the instructions on page 2 for student journals.

Student Directions

1. Choose a card.
2. Say the word.
3. Write the word with its missing letter in your journal.
4. Below the word, list all of the words you can make using some or all of the same letters.
5. Choose another card and repeat to find more hidden words.

What I Know (pages 56–57 and page 77)

Objective: Writing Letters, Words, and Sentences

Assembly Instructions
1. Copy activity page 56 or 57 onto colorful, sturdy paper.
2. Cut the page into strips.
3. Follow the instructions on page 2 for student journals.

Student Directions
1. Put the strips into the correct order to make a sentence.
2. Write the sentence in your journal.
3. Read the sentence to a friend.

You Earned It (pages 66 and 77)

Objective: Creative Writing

Assembly Instructions
1. Copy activity page 66 onto sturdy, green paper for each student.
2. Copy page 77 onto white paper for each student.
3. Cut the lined pages in half lengthwise.

Student Directions
1. Cut the green page lengthwise to make a front and back cover for your book.
2. Place the lined pages between the covers.
3. Staple the book along one short side.
4. Write this title on the first page: *How I Could Earn $100*. Then, write the story.
5. Share your story with a friend.

What's the Difference? (page 50)

Objective: Reading Aloud for Understanding

Assembly Instructions
1. Copy activity page 50 onto colorful, sturdy paper for each student.
2. Place several versions of the same stories in the center.

Student Directions
1. Find a partner.
2. Choose a story. You and your partner should read aloud different versions of the same story.
3. Talk about how the stories are the same and how they are different.
4. Together, fill in the Venn diagram.

Artist's Studio (pages 52–53 or 60–61)

Objective: Defining Vocabulary Words Visually

Assembly Instructions
1. Copy activity page 52, 53, 60, or 61 onto colorful, sturdy paper. Laminate for durability.
2. Cut the page into separate word cards.
3. Place the pictures in a plastic or paper bag.
4. Place paint, paintbrushes, construction paper, and the word cards in the center.

Student Directions
1. Draw a word card from the bag.
2. Paint a picture to describe the word.
3. Write the word under the painting.
4. Share your picture with a friend.

Readers' Nook (pages 78–79)

Objective: Encouraging Independent Reading

Assembly Instructions

1. Follow the instructions on page 2 for student ABC dictionaries.
2. Place several grade-appropriate books in the center.

Student Directions

1. Read a book.
2. Find the first important word in the title of the book (not "a" or "the").
3. Write the title of the book in the correct place in your ABC dictionary.
4. Try to find a book to read for each letter of the alphabet.
5. Write the titles in your ABC dictionary.

Describe It (pages 40 and 77)

Objective: Identifying Adjectives

Assembly Instructions

1. Copy activity page 40 onto white paper for each student.
2. Cut the page into separate picture cards.
3. Follow the instructions on page 2 for student journals.

Student Directions

1. Choose a picture card.
2. Color the picture and glue it in your journal.
3. Think of as many words as you can to describe the picture.
4. Write the words under the picture.
5. Share your list with a friend. Can your friend think of more describing words?
6. Choose another picture card and repeat.

Vocabulary Concentration (pages 38–40 or 51–53)

Objective: Building Vocabulary

Assembly Instructions

1. Copy activity page 40 and page 38 or 39 onto colorful, sturdy paper. Or, copy page 51 and page 52 or 53 onto colorful, sturdy paper. Laminate for durability.
2. Cut pages into separate word and picture cards.

Student Directions

1. Find a partner.
2. Place all of the cards facedown on a desktop.
3. Take turns. Turn over two cards at a time to find a matching picture and word.
4. If the two cards match, keep the cards and take another turn.
5. The player with the most cards wins.

Picture This! (pages 56–57)

Objective: Connecting Pictures with Written Words

Assembly Instructions

1. Copy activity page 56 or 57 onto colorful, sturdy paper.
2. Cut the page into strips and form the sentence.
3. Place magazines, glue, scissors, construction paper, and the sentence strip in the center.
4. Use the completed collages to create a class book.

Student Directions

1. Read the sentence.
2. Look in the magazines for pictures that show what the sentence says.
3. Cut out the pictures and glue them to construction paper.

Rhyme, Rhyme, Rhyme (pages 34–35 and 77)

Objective: Rhyming Words

Assembly Instructions

1. Copy activity page 34 or 35 onto colorful, sturdy paper. Laminate for durability.
2. Cut the page into separate cards.
3. Place the pictures in a plastic or paper bag.
4. Follow the instructions on page 2 for student journals.

Student Directions

1. Find a partner.
2. Draw a card from the bag.
3. Write the word in your journals.
4. Take turns thinking of words that rhyme with the word on the card.
5. Write the rhyming words in your journals.

Spell It, Check It (pages 28–29 or 32–33, and page 77)

Objective: Spelling Vocabulary Words

Assembly Instructions

1. Make two copies of activity page 28, 29, 32, or 33 onto colorful paper.
2. Cut one activity page into separate cards. Each card should feature a picture and its corresponding spelling choices. Glue each to a 3" x 5" (7.5 cm x 12.5 cm) index card.
3. Place the index cards in a paper or plastic bag.
4. Follow the instructions on page 2 for student journals.
5. Complete the other activity page to create an answer key. Laminate for durability.

Student Directions

1. Draw one card from the bag.
2. Choose the correct spelling of the word. Write the word in your journal.
3. Draw a picture of the word.
4. Choose another card and repeat.
5. Compare your words with a friend's words.
6. Check your words with the answer key. Fix any misspelled words.

Puzzle It Out (pages 74–75 and 78–79)

Objective: Recognizing Vocabulary Words

Assembly Instructions
1. Copy activity page 74 or 75 onto sturdy, white paper for each student.
2. Place crayons or markers, scissors, glue, construction paper, paper or plastic bags, and the pages in the center.
3. Follow the instructions on page 2 for student ABC dictionaries.

Student Directions
1. Choose a puzzle page. Color the picture.
2. Cut apart the puzzle pieces on the lines. Place all of the puzzle pieces in a bag.
3. Draw one puzzle piece from the bag. Read the word.
4. Write the word in your ABC dictionary.
5. Choose another puzzle piece. Repeat until you have chosen all of the pieces.
6. Put together the puzzle. Then, glue it to the construction paper.

Letter Scramble (pages 56–57 and 77)

Objective: Forming Words from Letters

Assembly Instructions
1. Copy activity page 56 or 57 onto colorful, sturdy paper. Laminate for durability.
2. Cut the words into separate letters.
3. Place the letters in a paper or plastic bag.
4. Copy page 77 onto white paper.

Student Directions
1. Find a partner.
2. Each of you should choose five letters from the bag.
3. First, work alone to make different words with the five letters each of you chose.
4. Write the words you make.
5. Then, work together to make more words with all 10 of the letters you and your partner chose.
6. Write the new words.

Picture This (pages 52–53 or 60–61)

Objective: Defining Vocabulary Words

Assembly Instructions

1. Copy activity page 52, 53, 60, or 61 onto colorful, sturdy paper. Laminate for durability.
2. Cut the words into separate cards.
3. Place the cards in a paper or plastic bag.
4. Place chalk and chalkboards or markers and chart paper and the bag in the center.

Student Directions

1. Find a partner.
2. Choose one card from the bag.
3. Read the word on the card but do not show it to your partner.
4. Draw a picture of the word.
5. Have your partner look at the picture to guess the word.
6. Change places and repeat with a new word.

It's Not the Same (pages 32–33 and 50)

Objective: Identifying Similarities and Differences

Assembly Instructions

1. Copy activity page 32 or 33 onto colorful, sturdy paper.
2. Cut each page into eight separate pictures. Do not use the word choices.
3. Place the pictures in a plastic or paper bag.
4. Copy page 50 onto white paper for each student.
5. Place glue, pencils, and the bag in the center.

Student Directions

1. Draw two picture cards from the bag.
2. Glue one picture to each side of the Venn diagram.
3. Fill in the Venn diagram with how the animals are the same and how they are different.
4. Share your Venn diagram with a friend.

Math

Learning Center Activities (pages 20–27)

I Am the Teacher (pages 46–49)

Objective: Telling Time

Assembly Instructions

1. Copy activity pages 46 and 47 and pages 48 and 49 back-to-back onto colorful, sturdy paper. Laminate for durability.
2. Cut the pages into separate cards.

Student Directions

1. Find two partners. You will be the "teacher."
2. Show the clock on a card to your partners.
3. Give the card to the player who says the right time first.
4. Repeat with all of the cards.
5. The player who has the most cards is the next "teacher."

Money Concentration (pages 67–69)

Objective: Understanding Money Values

Assembly Instructions

1. Copy activity page 67 and page 68 or 69 onto colorful, sturdy paper. Laminate for durability.
2. Cut pages into separate word and picture cards.

Student Directions

1. Find a partner.
2. Place all of the cards facedown on a desktop.
3. Take turns. Turn over two cards at a time to find a matching picture and word.
4. If the two cards match, keep the cards and take another turn.
5. The player with the most cards wins.

Odd or Even? (pages 58–59 and 77)

Objectives: Counting; Recognizing Odd and Even Amounts

Assembly Instructions

1. Copy activity page 58 or 59 onto colorful, sturdy paper. Laminate for durability.
2. Cut the page into separate picture cards. Do not use the number choices.
3. Label two plastic cups, one with the word "odd" and the other "even."
4. Place the cups and cards in the center.
5. Follow the instructions on page 2 for student journals.

Student Directions

1. Choose a card. Count the dots on the card.
2. Decide if the number is odd or even.
3. Put the card in the correct cup.
4. Repeat with the rest of the cards.
5. Count how many cards are in each cup.
6. Write the number of odd cards and the number of even cards in your journal.

Favorite Time Mobile (pages 42, 46, and 48)

Objective: Telling Time

Assembly Instructions

1. Copy activity page 42 onto colorful paper for each student. Note: You may wish to complete the clock faces as a whole-class activity.
2. Copy the picture card activity pages 46 and 48 onto colorful, sturdy paper for each student. Cut the pictures into separate cards.
3. Place paper plates, glue, scissors, yarn, tape, crayons or markers, cards, and the activity pages in the center.

Student Directions

1. Color the large clock, hands, and numbers. Cut them out.
2. Glue the clock face to a paper plate. Glue the clock numbers in the correct places.
3. Think about your favorite time of day. Glue the clock hands to show your favorite time.
4. Choose three clock picture cards that show other times of the day that you like.
5. Write the correct time on the back of each clock picture card.
6. Attach the cards to the paper plate clock with yarn and tape.

Food Story Problems (pages 72–73 and 77)

Objective: Solving Story Problems

Assembly Instructions

1. Copy activity page 72 or 73 onto colorful, sturdy paper. Laminate for durability.
2. Cut the page into separate story problem strips.
3. Follow the instructions on page 2 for student journals.

Student Directions

1. Find a partner.
2. Choose a story problem. Work together to find the answer.
3. Write in your journals how you solved the problem.
4. Repeat with another story problem.

My Time Book (pages 43–45)

Objectives: Telling Time; Understanding Time of Day

Assembly Instructions

1. Copy activity page 44 or 45 onto sturdy, white paper for each student. Have plain sheets of sturdy paper available for the back covers of the time books.
2. Copy activity page 43 onto white paper. Make four copies for each student.

Student Directions

1. Color the front cover of your book about time and write your name.
2. On the lined paper, draw hands on the clock to show a time of day.
3. Write what happens at that time of day.
4. Repeat to make three more pages.
5. Place the lined pages between covers to make a book.
6. Staple the book along the left side.
7. Share your book with a friend.

Time-to-Match Journal (pages 46–49 and 77)

Objective: Telling Time

Assembly Instructions

1. Copy activity pages 46–47 and/or 48–49 onto colorful paper, one of each set for each student.
2. Place glue, scissors, and the activity pages in the center.
3. Follow the instructions on page 2 for student journals.

Student Directions

1. Cut the pages into separate time and clock picture cards.
2. Place all of the cards faceup on a desktop.
3. Choose a clock picture card.
4. Find the time card that matches the clock.
5. Glue the matching time and clock picture cards to the same page in your journal.
6. Repeat with all of the cards.

Spider Number Sentences (pages 76-77)

Objective: Creating Number Sentences

Assembly Instructions

1. Make two copies of activity page 76 on colorful, sturdy paper. Laminate for durability.
2. Cut each page into six cards.
3. Follow the instructions on page 2 for student journals.

Student Directions

1. Find a partner.
2. Place all of the spider cards faceup on a desktop.
3. Choose two cards. Count the spiders on the cards and add them together.
4. Write the number sentence in your journal.
5. Repeat with two different cards each time. Write each number sentence in your journal.

Time in a Bag (pages 41, 47, 49, and 77)

Objective: Telling Time

Assembly Instructions

1. Copy activity pages 47 and 49 onto colorful, sturdy paper. Laminate for durability.
2. Cut the pages into separate time cards. Then, cut each card into two pieces, separating the hour and colon from the minutes.
3. Label two paper bags, one with the word "hours" and the other "minutes."
4. Sort the hour and minute cards into the paper bags.
5. Copy activity pages 41 and 77 onto white paper for each student.
6. Place crayons or markers, glue, scissors, the activity pages, and the paper bags in the center.

Student Directions

1. Choose one card from the "hours" bag. Then, choose one card from the "minutes" bag.
2. Draw hands on a clock to show the time on the cards.
3. Cut out the clock. Glue it to the lined paper.
4. Write the time under the clock.
5. Repeat until all of the clocks are filled in.

Graph the Letters (pages 34–35)

Objective: Creating a Bar Graph

Assembly Instructions

1. Copy activity page 34 or 35 onto colorful, sturdy paper. Laminate for durability.
2. Cut the page into separate cards. Each card should feature a picture and its corresponding word.
3. Place the cards in a paper or plastic bag.
4. Place masking tape and the bag in the center.
5. Make a five-column bar graph on bulletin board paper. Label the columns as follows: column one—*3 letters or less*; column two—*4 letters*; column three—*5 letters*; column four—*6 letters*; and column five—*7 letters or more*.

Student Directions

1. Draw one card from the bag.
2. Read the word. Count the number of letters in the word.
3. Find the column on the bar graph with the same number.
4. Tape the card to the correct column on the bar graph.
5. Repeat with all of the cards.

Money Match (pages 64–65)

Objective: Identifying Coin Values

Assembly Instructions
1. Copy activity page 64 or 65 onto colorful, sturdy paper. Laminate for durability.
2. Cut the page into separate number cards and picture cards.

Student Directions
1. Find a partner.
2. Place the number cards and picture cards faceup on a desktop.
3. Take turns. Choose a picture card.
4. Find the number card that matches the picture.
5. Repeat until all of the cards have been matched.

How Many Letters? (pages 70–71 and 77)

Objective: Counting to Nine

Assembly Instructions
1. Copy activity page 70 or 71 onto colorful, sturdy paper. Laminate for durability.
2. Cut the page into separate cards. Each card should feature a picture and its corresponding word.
3. Place the cards and a variety of books of different reading levels in the center.
4. Follow the instructions on page 2 for student journals.

Student Directions
1. Choose a card.
2. Read the word. Count the number of letters.
3. If the word has six letters, write the word in your journal.
4. Repeat with all of the cards.
5. Choose a book.
6. Look for words with six letters.
7. Write the words in your journal.

Spending Spree (pages 66 and 77)

Objective: Adding Money

Assembly Instructions
1. Copy activity page 66 onto sturdy, green paper for each student.
2. Copy page 77 onto white paper for each student.
3. Cut the lined pages in half lengthwise.
4. Place scissors, glue, and an assortment of advertising flyers in the center.

Student Directions
1. Cut the green page lengthwise to make a front and back cover for your book.
2. Place the lined pages between the covers.
3. Staple the book along one short side.
4. Look at the advertisements. Choose at least three items you would like to buy.
5. Add the prices of the items. If the total is less than $100, cut out the items.
6. Glue the items in your book. Write the number sentence.

Food Find (pages 70–71 and 77)

Objective: Creating a Bar Graph

Assembly Instructions
1. Copy activity page 70 or 71 onto colorful, sturdy paper. Laminate for durability.
2. Cut the page into separate cards. Each card should feature a picture and its corresponding word.
3. Copy page 77 onto white paper for each student.
4. Place masking tape and the cards in the center.
5. Make a four-column bar graph on bulletin board paper. Label the columns as follows: column one—*fruits*; column two—*vegetables*; column three—*grains*; and column four—*meats*.

Student Directions
1. Choose a card.
2. Look at the picture. Read the word.
3. Decide if the food is a fruit, vegetable, grain, or meat.
4. Find the correct column on the bar graph.
5. Tape the card to the correct column.
6. Repeat with all of the cards.
7. Write how many foods are in each column.

It's Time (pages 47 and 49)

Objective: Understanding Time of Day

Assembly Instructions

1. Copy activity pages 47 and 49 onto colorful, sturdy paper. Laminate for durability.
2. Cut the pages into separate cards.
3. Place the cards in a paper or plastic bag.

Student Directions

1. Find a partner.
2. Take turns. Choose one card from the bag.
3. Read the time on the card.
4. Tell your partner what you were doing yesterday at that time of day.
5. Repeat with the rest of the cards.

Dollars and Cents (pages 67–69 and 77)

Objective: Identifying Money Values

Assembly Instructions

1. Copy activity page 67 and 68 or 69 onto colorful paper for each student.
2. Follow the instructions on page 2 for student journals.
3. Place glue, scissors, markers or crayons, and the cards in the center.

Student Directions

1. Cut the pages into separate word and picture cards.
2. Place all of the cards faceup on a desktop.
3. Choose a picture card.
4. Find the word card that matches the picture.
5. Glue the matching cards together in your journal.
6. Write the numeral for the same amount of money next to the picture.
7. Repeat until all of the cards have been matched.

Nombre: ___________________________

Deletrea correctamente

Haz un círculo alrededor de la palabra correcta de cada grupo.

canjrejo
cangrejo
canjrego

cabillitos de mar
cabalitos de mar
caballito de mar

eanguila
anguilae
anguila

tiburon
tiburón
tiborón

delfíne
delfín
dolfin

ballena
balena
baleña

pulpo
polpo
poulpo

estrella de mar
estrela de mar
estrella del mar

Name: ______________________________

Spell It Correctly

Circle the word that is spelled correctly in each group.

krab
krabb
crab

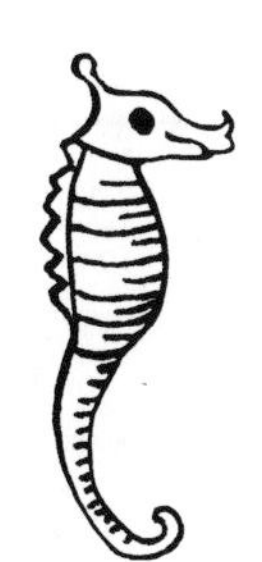

see horse
sea horse
sea hors

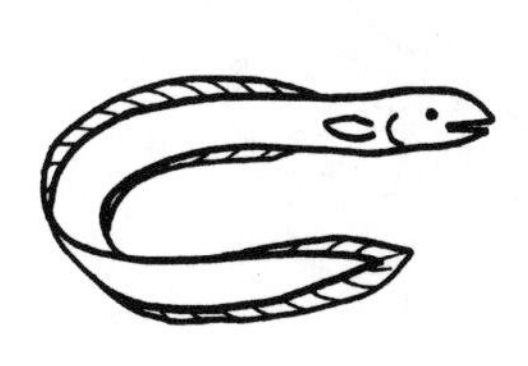

eeel
eele
eel

sharck
shark
sharc

dolphine
dolphin
dolfin

whale
wale
wail

octopus
ockopus
ocktopus

starfish
star fish
star fiss

Nombre: ______________________________

Llena los espacios

Escribe la letra que falta en cada palabra.

__angrejo

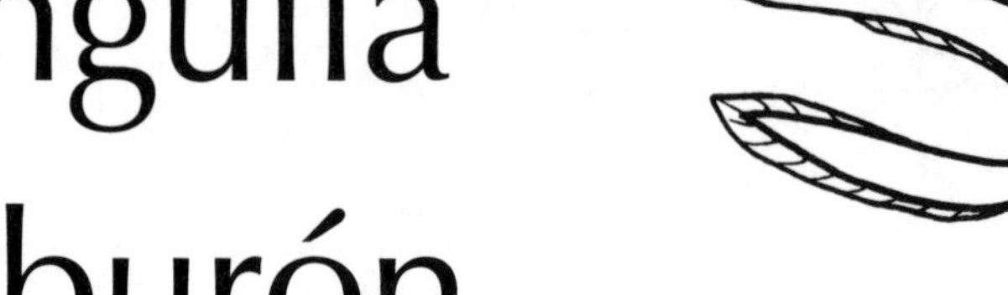

__nguila

__iburón

__ulpo

__oca

__strella de mar

__elfín

__aballito de mar

__allena

__céano

Name: ____________________

Fill in the Blanks

Fill in the missing letter in each word.

___rab

___el

___hark

___ctopus

___eal

___tarfish

___olphin

___ea horse

___hale

___cean

Nombre: ______________________________

Deletrea correctamente

Haz un círculo alrededor de la palabra correcta de cada grupo.

caballo
cabalo
cabbalo

vaca
baca
vacca

elefanti
elefante
alafant

lyon
león
lion

perro
pero
pere

cato
gato
gatto

pájarro
pojoro
pájaro

mono
moño
monoo

Name: ______________________________

Spell It Correctly

Circle the word that is spelled correctly in each group.

horse
hoerse
hors

kow
cowe
cow

elefant
elephant
eleffant

lyon
lion
lien

dog
dogg
dawg

cat
katt
cot

byrd
bierd
bird

munkey
monkey
monkee

pájaro
camello
gato
ballena
vaca
foca
perro
elefante
rana

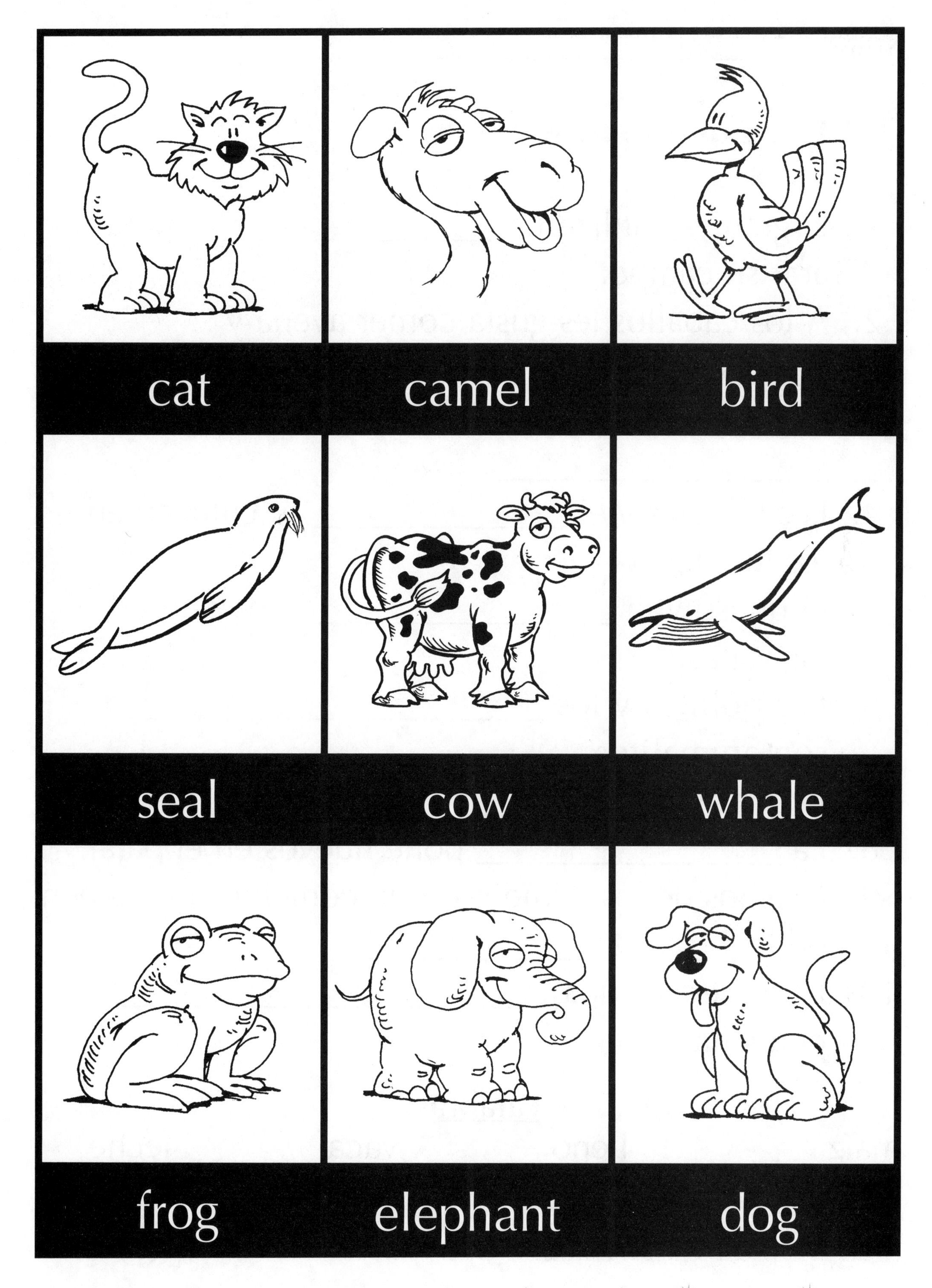
cat
camel
bird
seal
cow
whale
frog
elephant
dog

Nombre: ______________________________

Llena los espacios

Usa las palabras de abajo para completar cada oración.

1. El granjero utiliza un ____________________ para arar su campo.
2. A los caballos les gusta comer avena y ____________________.
3. El granjero mantiene el heno seco en el ____________________.
4. Los tomates y el ________________ se cultivan en los huertos.
5. El queso y la ____________________ provienen de las vacas.
6. Los pollitos y los ____________________________ son animalitos.
7. El potro es un __________________________ pequeño.
8. La ____________________ pone huevos en el pajar.
9. Muchos de los alimentos que comemos provienen de la ______________________.
10. La ternera es una ______________________________ pequeña.

Palabras:

maíz	heno	vaca	leche
cerditos	tractor	caballo	granja
granero	gallina		

Name: ______________________________

Farm Fill in the Blanks

Use the word bank below to complete each sentence.

1. The farmer uses the ________________ to plow his fields.
2. Horses like to eat oats and ______________.
3. The farmer keeps the hay dry in the ___________________.
4. Tomatoes and ______________ grow in the fields.
5. Cheese and ________________ come from cows.
6. Chicks and __________________ are baby animals.
7. A foal is a baby ___________________.
8. The _________________ lays eggs in the hay.
9. Many of the foods we eat come from the ____________________.
10. A calf is a baby __________________.

Words:

corn	hay	cow	milk
piglets	tractor	horse	farm
barn	chicken		

cerdo

tiburón

caballo

león

pulpo

mono

shark

pig

lion

horse

monkey

octopus

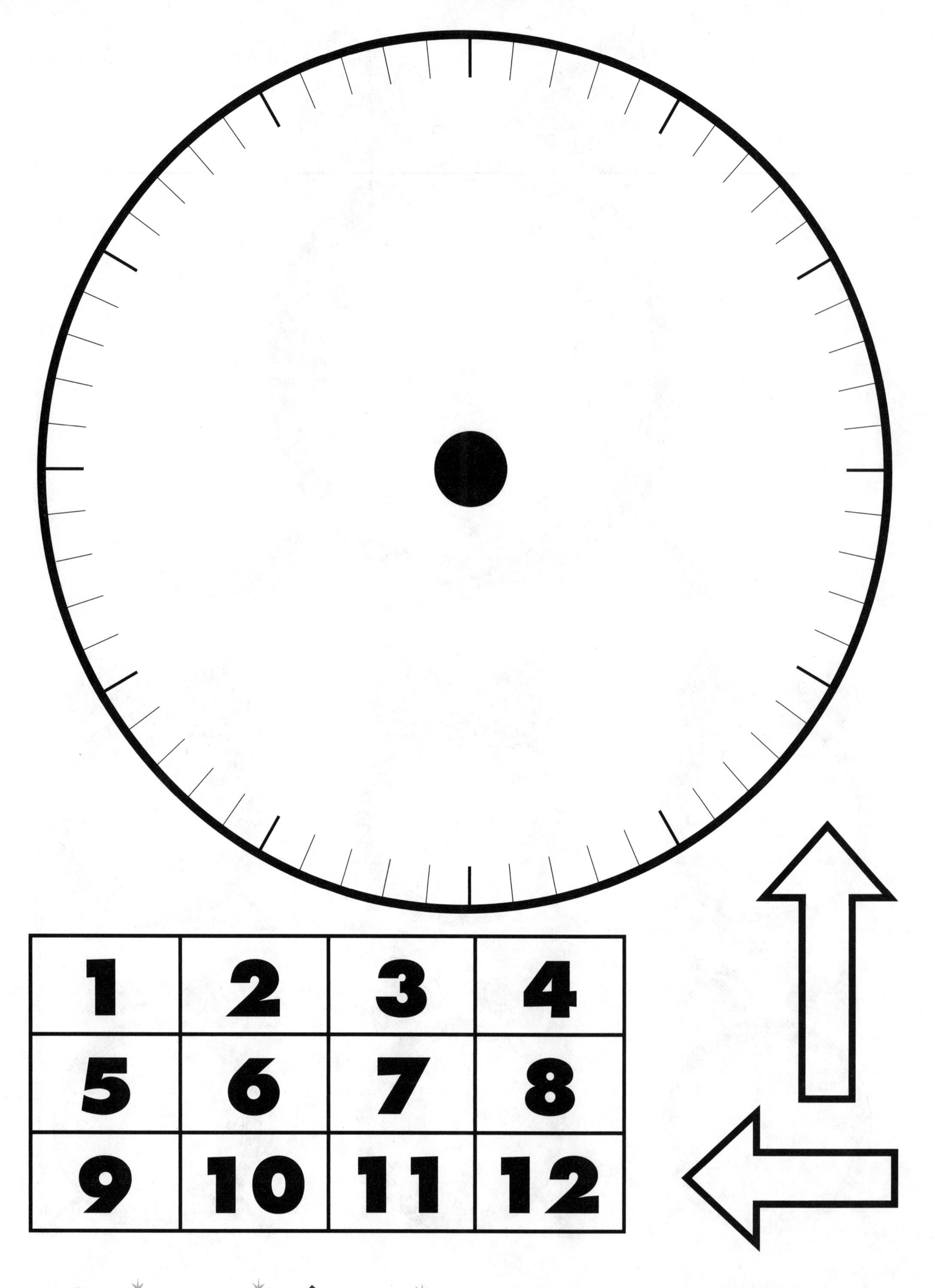
1
2
3
4
5
6
7
8
9
10
11
12

12
1
2
3
4
5
6
7
8
9
10
11

Mi libro de

La hora

Nombre: ______________________

My

Time Book

Name: ______________________

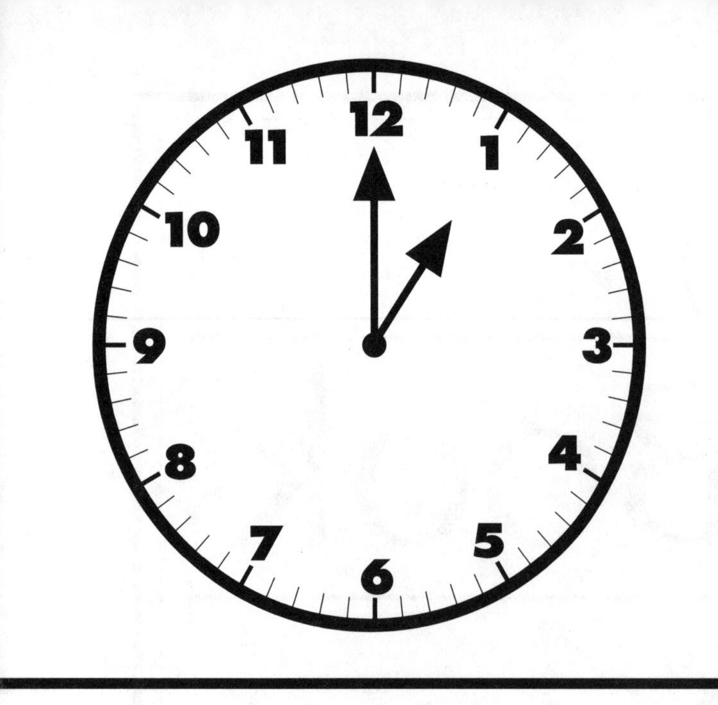
12
1
2
3
4
5
6
7
8
9
10
11

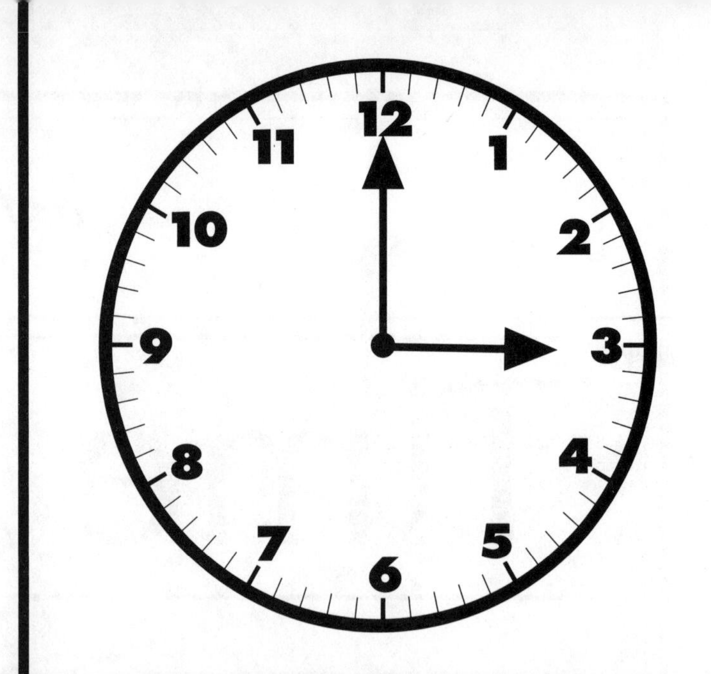
12
1
2
3
4
5
6
7
8
9
10
11

12
1
2
3
4
5
6
7
8
9
10
11

12
1
2
3
4
5
6
7
8
9
10
11

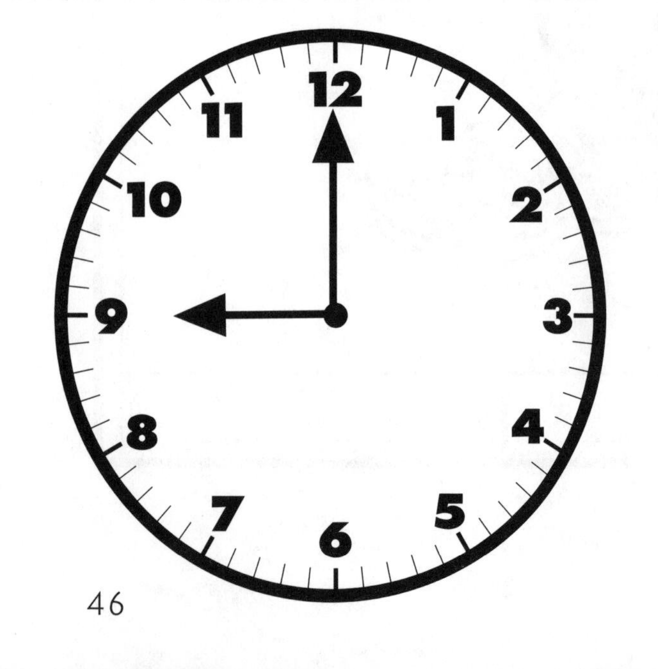
12
1
2
3
4
5
6
7
8
9
10
11

12
1
2
3
4
5
6
7
8
9
10
11

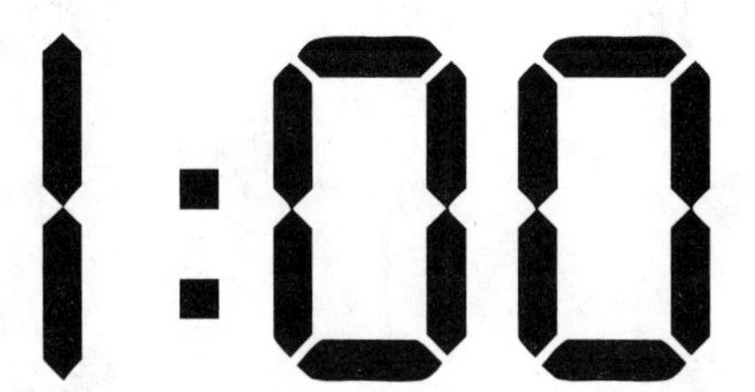

7:00

5:00

11:00

9:00

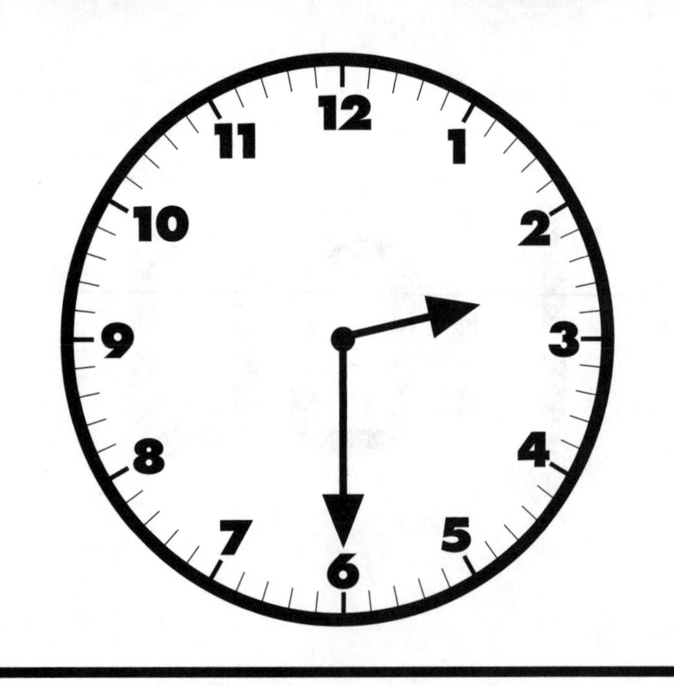
12
1
2
3
4
5
6
7
8
9
10
11

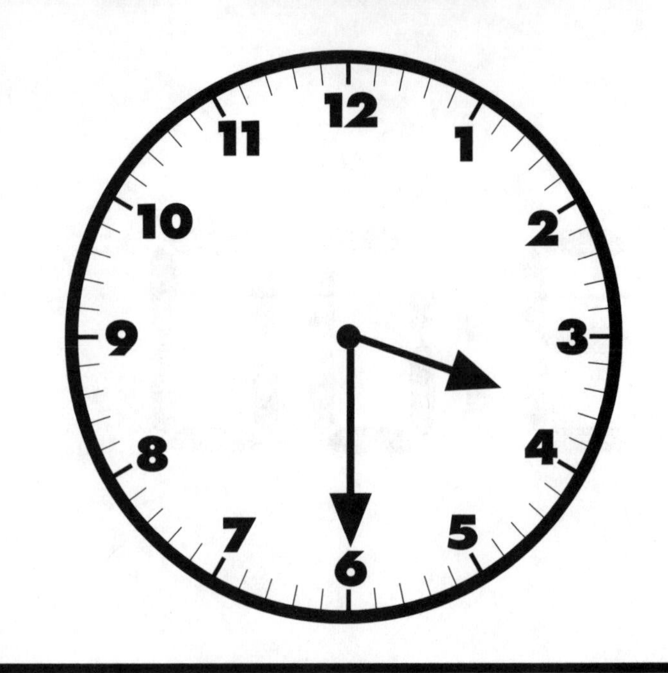
12
1
2
3
4
5
6
7
8
9
10
11

12
1
2
3
4
5
6
7
8
9
10
11

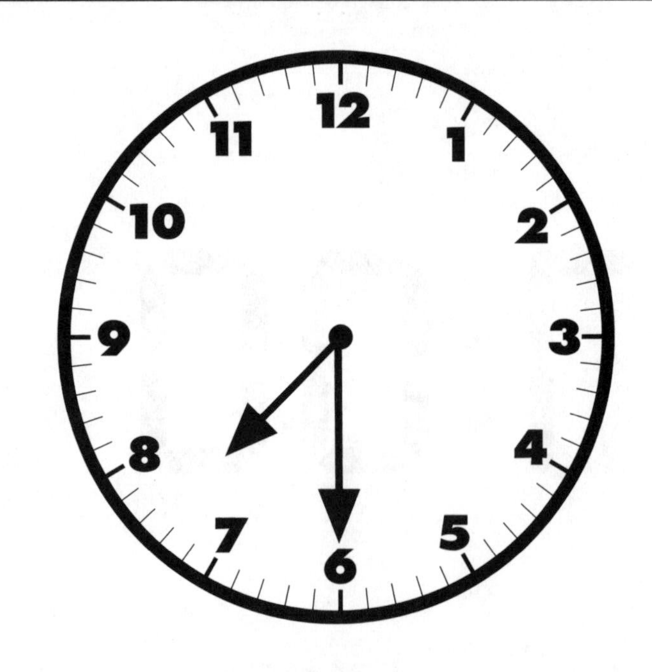
12
1
2
3
4
5
6
7
8
9
10
11

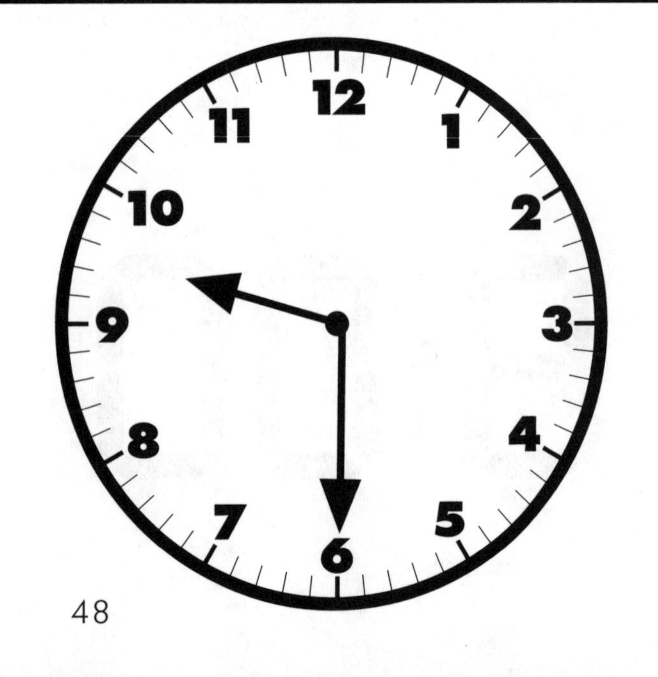
12
1
2
3
4
5
6
7
8
9
10
11

12
1
2
3
4
5
6
7
8
9
10
11

3:30	2:30
7:30	4:30
11:30	9:30

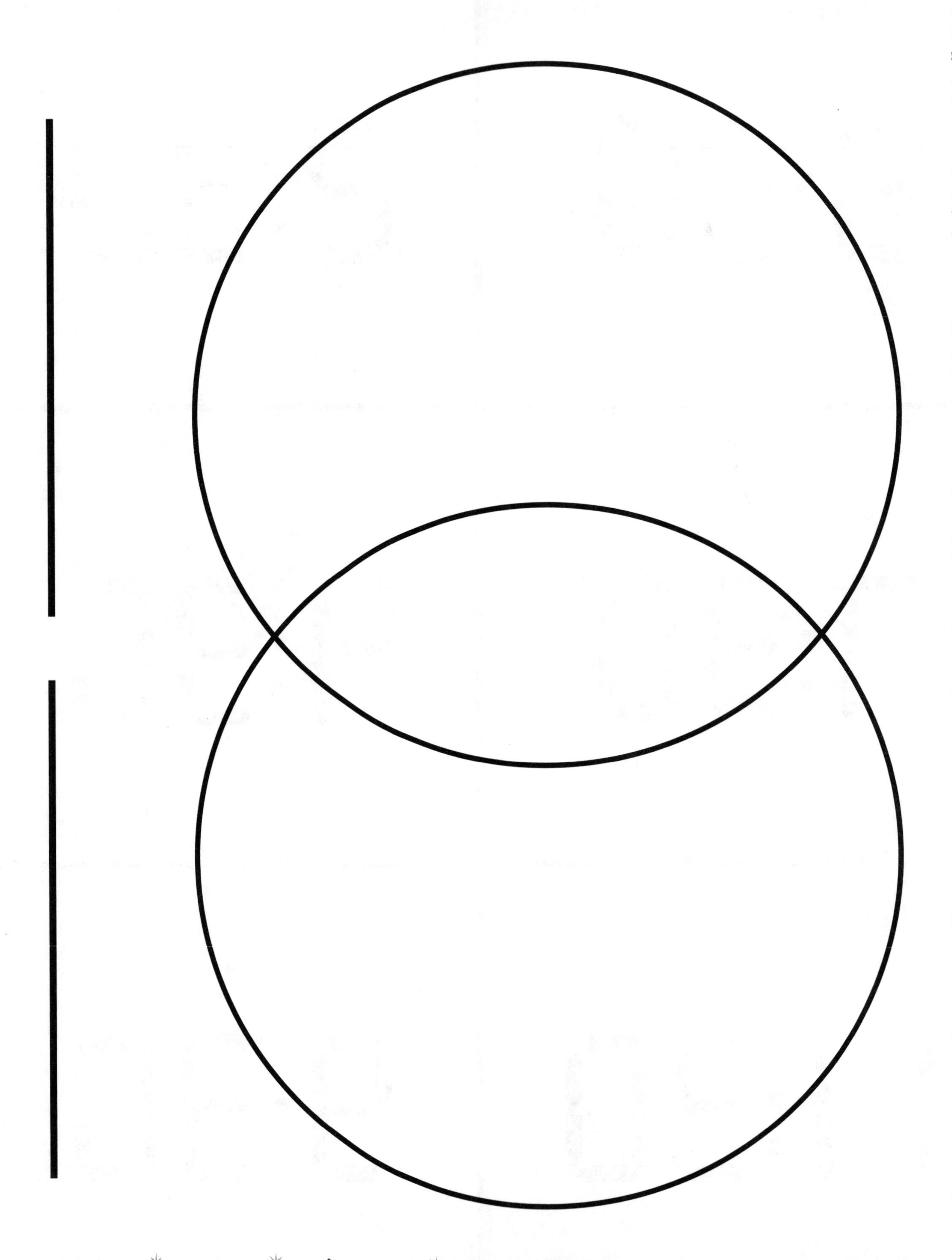

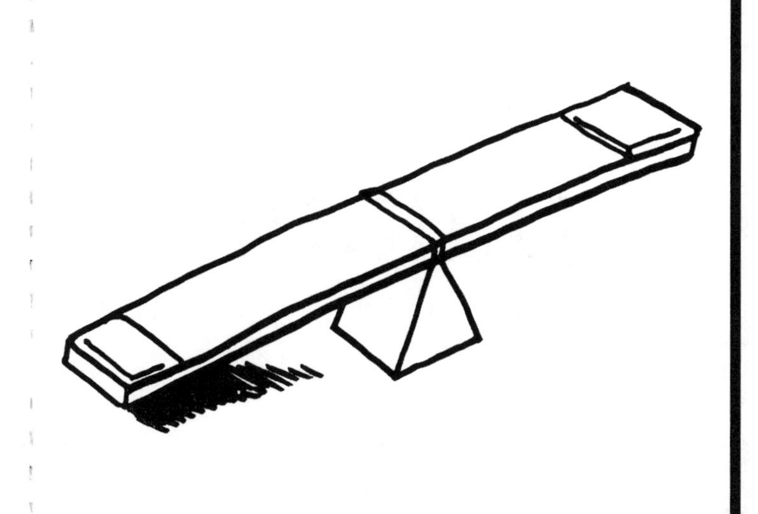

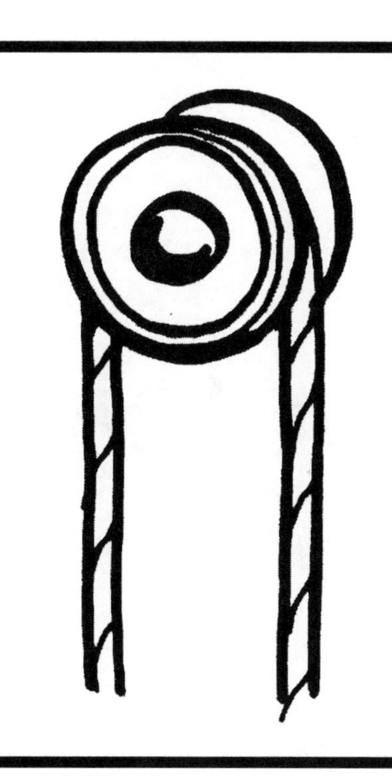

rueda y eje

palanca

plano inclinado

polea

tornillo

cuña

lever	wheel and axle
pulley	inclined plane
wedge	screw

Móviles de las máquinas sencillas

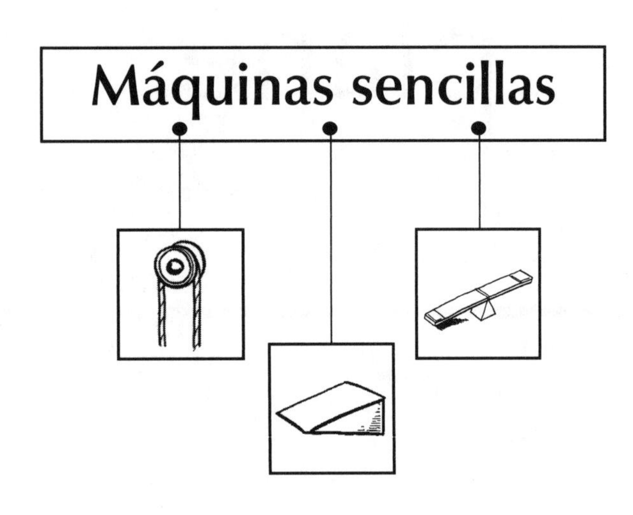

Máquinas sencillas

Máquinas sencillas

Simple Machine Mobiles

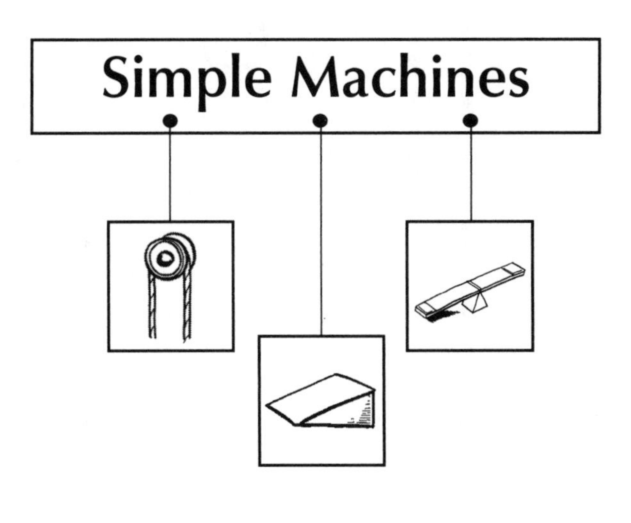

Simple Machines

Simple Machines

Planos inclinados

o rampas se usan para

mover y levantar objetos.

Inclined planes

or ramps are used to

move and lift objects.

Nombre: ______________________________

Cuenta los puntos

Haz un círculo alrededor de la cantidad correcta.

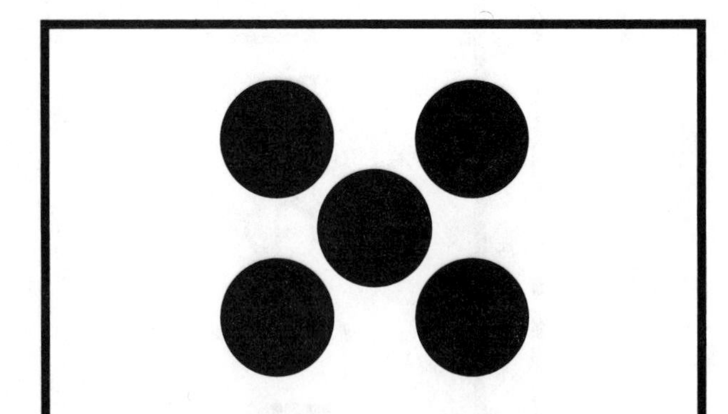

5 3

7 3

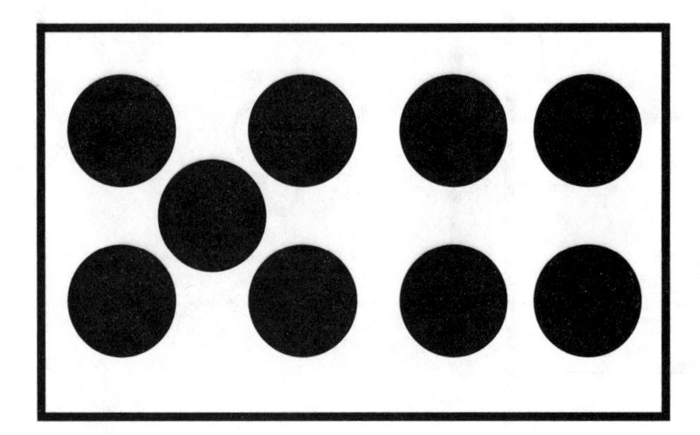

9 7

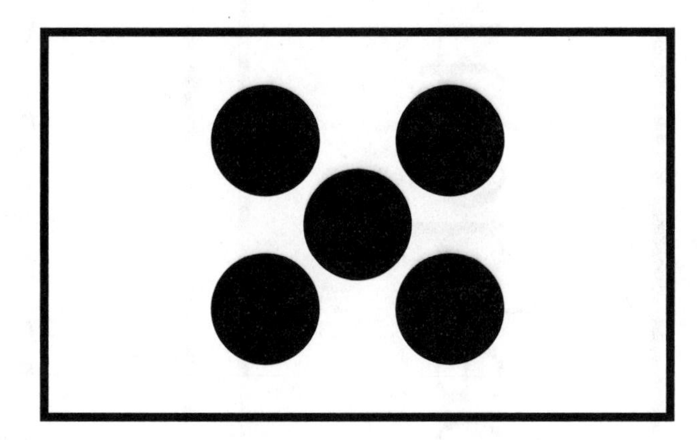

1 5

3 1

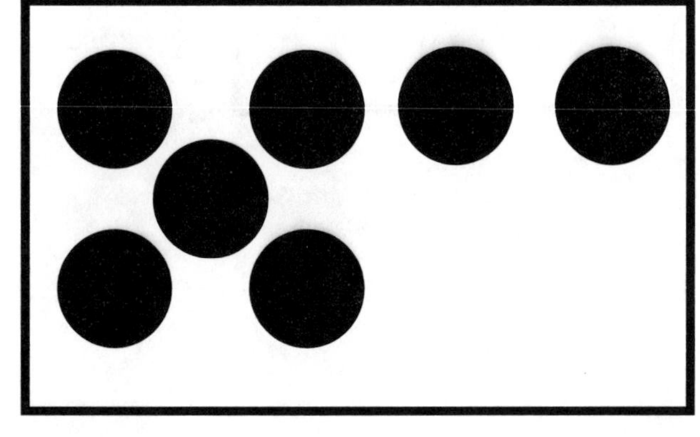

7 5

Name: ______________________________

Count the Dots

Circle the correct amount.

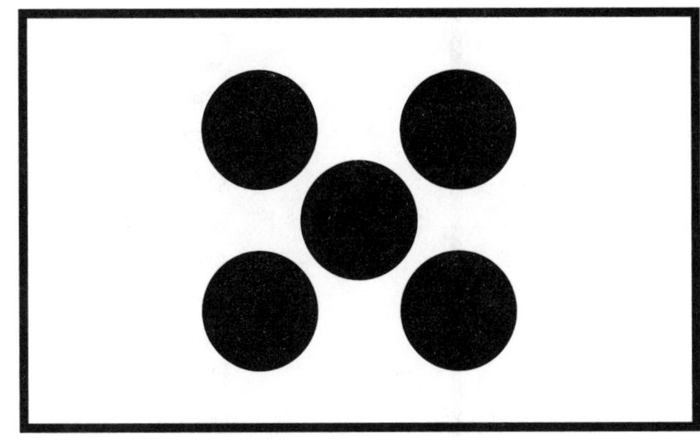

5 3

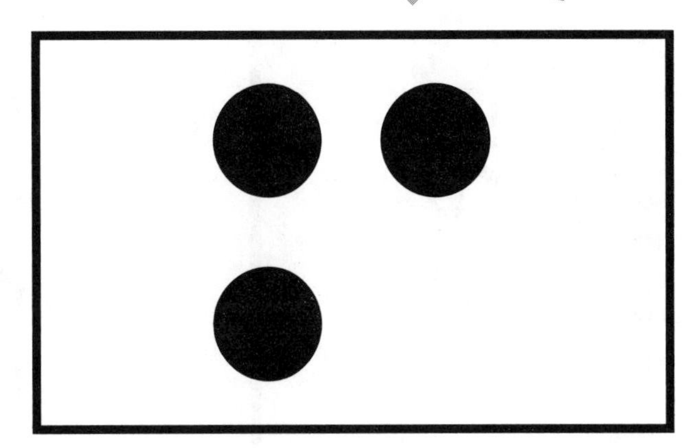

7 3

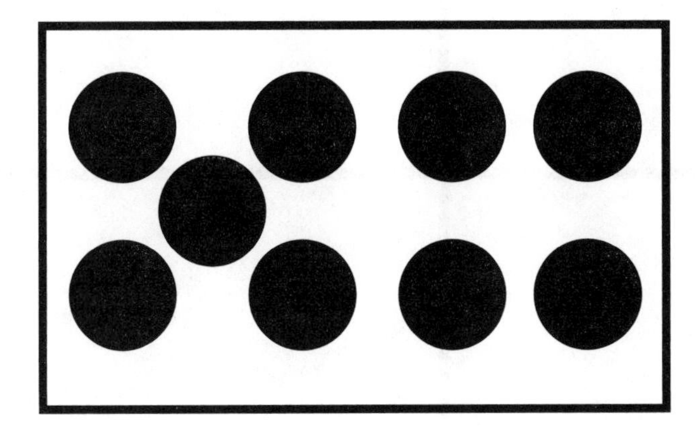

9 7

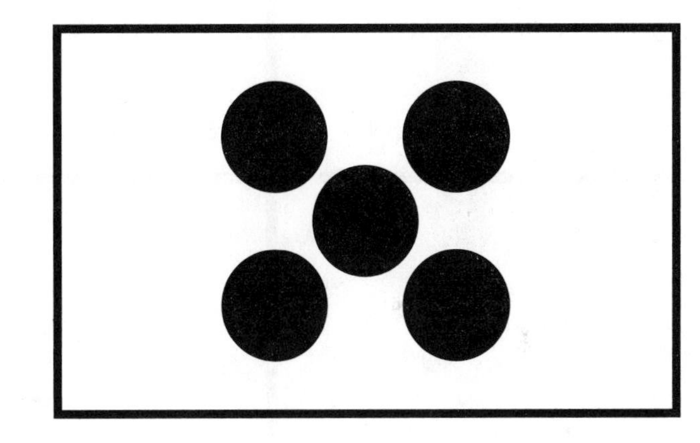

1 5

3 1

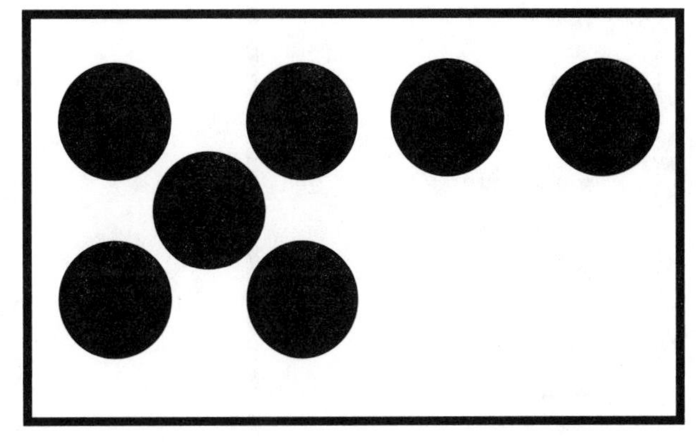

7 5

constelación	galaxia
luna nueva	sistema solar
cuarto creciente	luna llena

constellation

galaxy

new moon

solar system

crescent moon

full moon

Nombre: ____________________

Llena los espacios

Escribe la letra que falta en cada palabra.

do__tora

bombe__o

merca__o

boca de ag__a

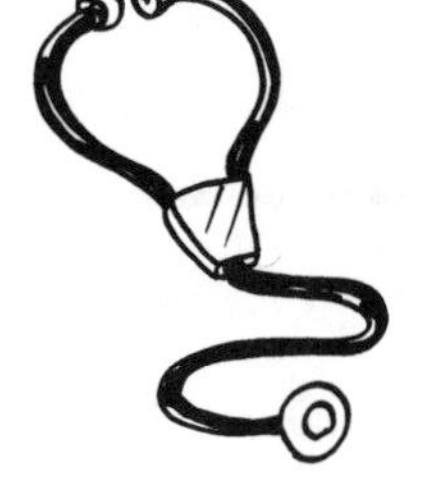

estet__scopio

pla__a

v__veres

carte__o

hos__ital

car__a

Name: ______________________

Fill in the Blanks

Fill in the missing letter in each word.

do__tor

fire__ighter

grocery s__ore

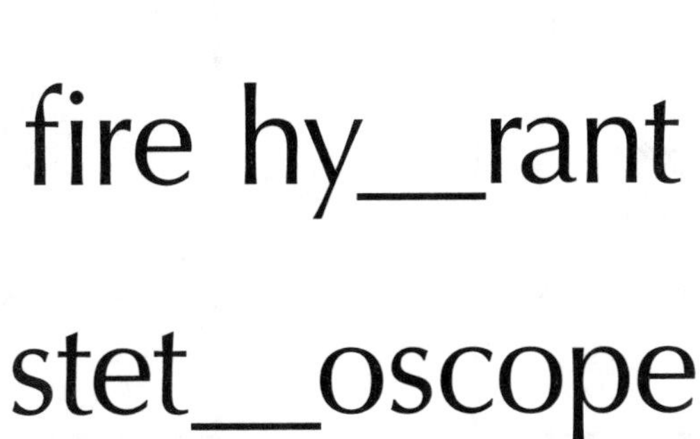

fire hy__rant

stet__oscope

bad__e

g__oceries

mail carr__er

hos__ital

let__er

Nombre: ______________________________

Mezcla de dinero

Traza una línea desde la cantidad escrita hasta las monedas correctas.

$1.12

$1.05

95¢

56¢

Name: ______________________________

Money Mix

Draw a line from the money amount to the correct coins.

Amount	Coins
$1.12	
$1.05	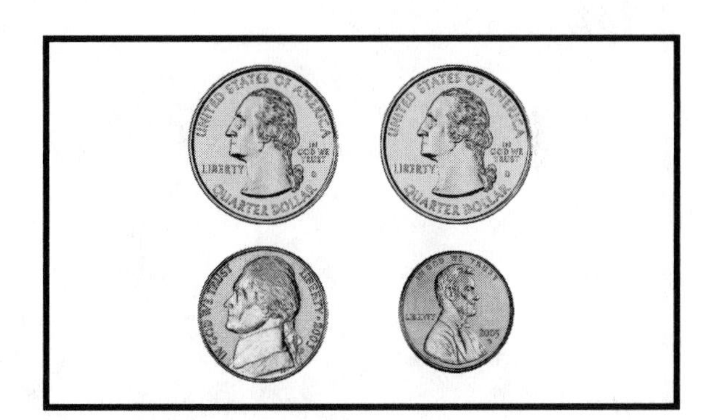
95¢	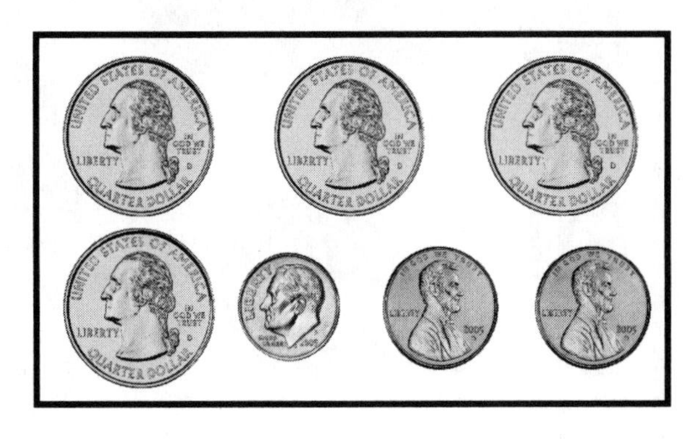
56¢	

FEDERAL RESERVE NOTE
DD 18988915 A
D4
THIS NOTE IS LEGAL TENDER
FOR ALL DEBTS, PUBLIC AND PRIVATE
Treasurer of the United States.
SERIES
2003
100
FRANKLIN
DD 18988915 A
Secretary of the Treasury.
ONE HUNDRED DOLLARS

FEDERAL RESERVE NOTE
DD 18988915 A
D4
THIS NOTE IS LEGAL TENDER
FOR ALL DEBTS, PUBLIC AND PRIVATE
Treasurer of the United States.
SERIES
2003
100
FRANKLIN
DD 18988915 A
Secretary of the Treasury.
ONE HUNDRED DOLLARS

IN GOD WE TRUST
LIBERTY
2005
D

IN GOD WE TRUST
LIBERTY
2003
D

LIBERTY
IN GOD WE TRUST
P
2005

UNITED STATES OF AMERICA
IN GOD WE TRUST
LIBERTY
D
QUARTER DOLLAR

FEDERAL RESERVE NOTE
THE UNITED STATES OF AMERICA
THIS NOTE IS LEGAL TENDER FOR ALL DEBTS, PUBLIC AND PRIVATE
A 23452892 D
WASHINGTON, D.C.
A
A 23452892 D
ONE DOLLAR

FEDERAL RESERVE NOTE
THE UNITED STATES OF AMERICA
DL 09487209 C
L12
THIS NOTE IS LEGAL TENDER FOR ALL DEBTS, PUBLIC AND PRIVATE
DL 09487209 C
FIVE DOLLARS

moneda
de cinco
centavos
“nickel”

moneda de
un centavo
“penny”

moneda de
25 centavos
“quarter”

moneda de
10 centavos
“dime”

cinco
dólares

dólar

penny

nickel

dime

quarter

one dollar

five dollars

zanahoria
pan
manzana
uvas
lechuga
jamón
tomate
maíz
panecillo
bistec
naranja
banana

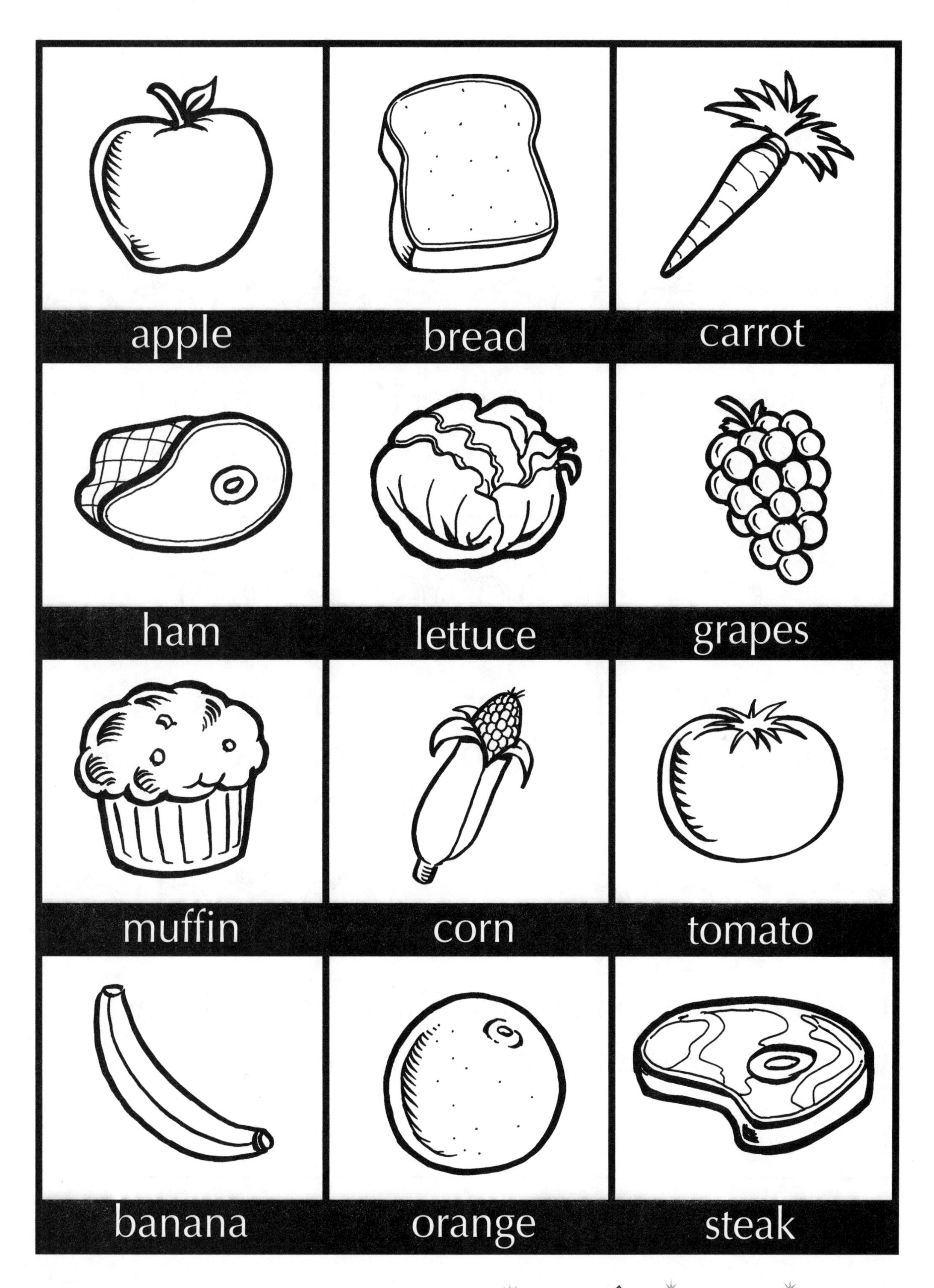
apple
bread
carrot
ham
lettuce
grapes
muffin
corn
tomato
banana
orange
steak

Nombre: ______________________________

Problemas con alimentos

Resuelve cada problema y muestra tu trabajo.

Tomás tenía una bolsa con 10 manzanas. Le dio 2 a Marcos y 4 a José. ¿Cuántas manzanas tiene Tomás ahora? ______________________

Pon una "X" en la tercera manzana a la izquierda. Colorea de rojo la primera manzana. Colorea de verde la segunda manzana.

Linda tiene 4 manzanas. Ella escogió 5 más. Escribe la ecuación y la respuesta.

____

Name: ______________________________

Food Story Problems

Complete each problem and show your work.

Tom had a bag of 10 apples. He gave 2 to Tim and 4 to Jason. How many apples does Tom have left? ______________________________

Put an "X" on the apple that is third from the left. Color the first apple red. Color the second apple green.

Linda had 4 apples. She picked 5 more. How many does she have total? Write the equation and answer.

____

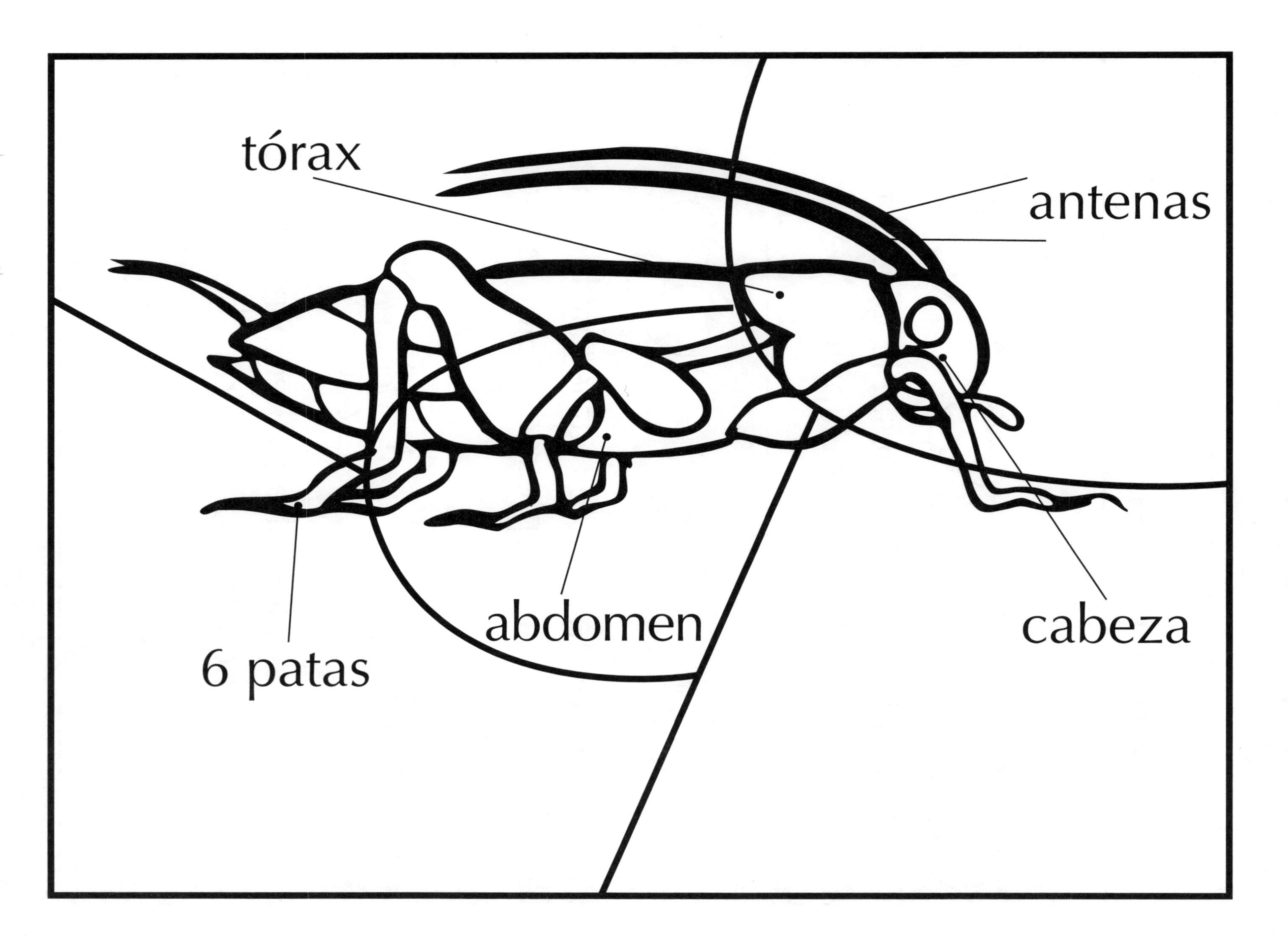
tórax
antenas
abdomen
cabeza
6 patas

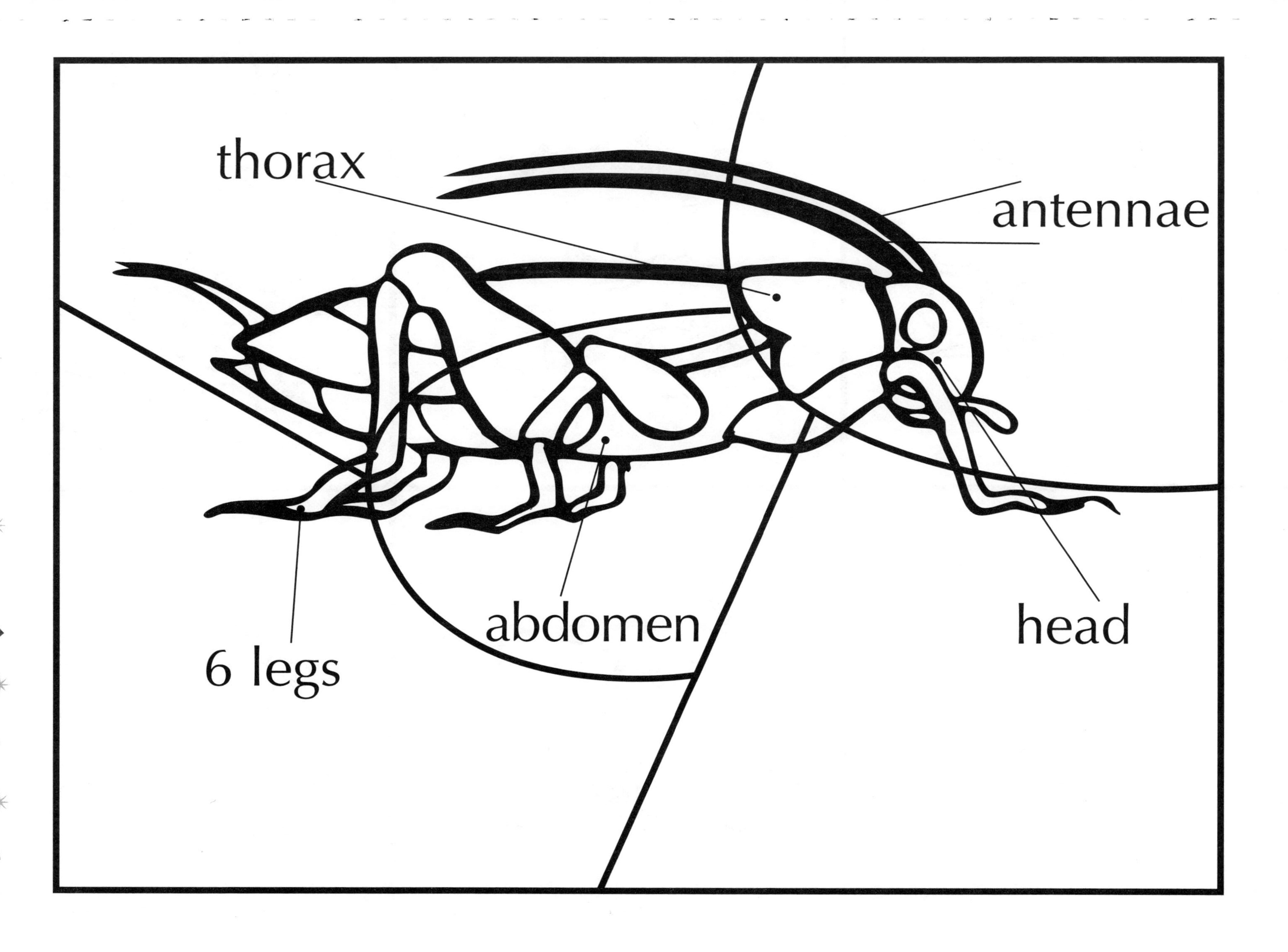
thorax
antennae
abdomen
head
6 legs

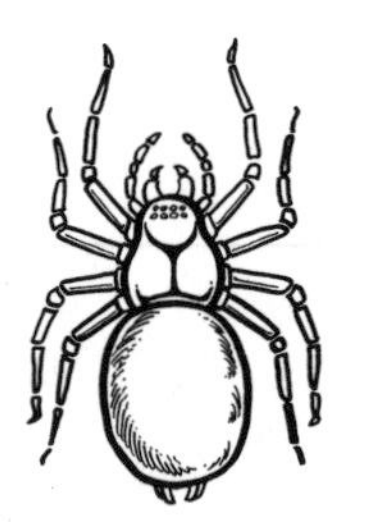

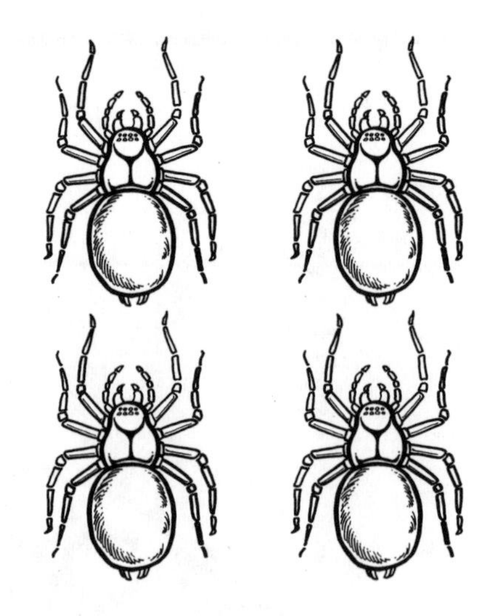

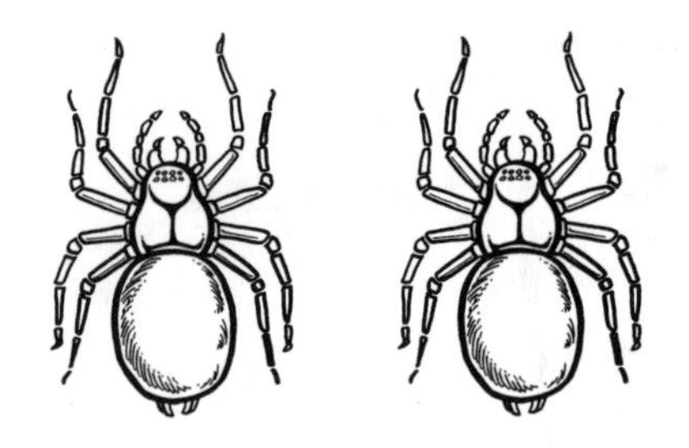

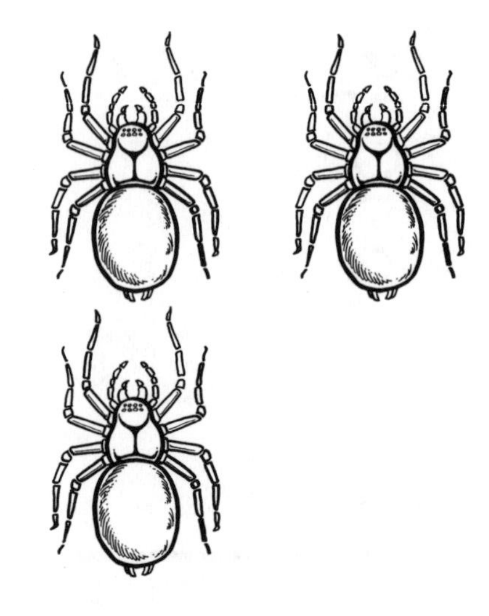